# CRATER LAKE
# NATIONAL PARK
# ACTIVITY BOOK

## PUZZLES, MAZES, GAMES, AND MORE ABOUT
## CRATER LAKE NATIONAL PARK

## NATIONAL PARKS ACTIVITIES SERIES

# CRATER LAKE NATIONAL PARK ACTIVITY BOOK

Copyright 2021
Published by Little Bison Press

The author acknowledges that the land on which Crater Lake National Park is located are the traditional lands of Klamath and Molalla tribes and the Confederated Tribes of Grand Ronde and Siletz Indians.

LITTLE BISON

Press

For more free national parks activities, visit
www.littlebisonpress.com

# About Crater Lake National Park

Crater Lake National Park is located in the state of Oregon. Crater Lake has inspired the awe and wonder of people from all over the world. The lake was formed over 7,700 years ago when Mount Mazama, an active volcano, erupted and collapsed.

At 1,943 feet deep, Crater Lake is the deepest lake in America. Famous for its beautiful blue color, the lake's water comes directly from snow or rain. There are no inlets from other water sources. It is because of this that no mineral deposits or sediment are carried into the lake, helping maintain its rich color and making it one of the cleanest lakes in the world. Visitors can swim at designated areas, but beware - the water is usually very cold!

Visitors can visit The Sinnott Memorial Overlook. It offers one of the finest views of Crater Lake. You can peer down a sheer drop of nearly 900 feet to the shore.

Crater Lake National Park is famous for:
- deep, clear blue lake
- wildlife viewing
- its rich and mysterious history

Hey! I'm Parker!

I'm the only snail in history to visit every National Park in the United States! Come join me on my adventures in Crater Lake National Park.

Throughout this book, we will learn about the history of the park, the animals and plants that live here, and and things to do if you ever visit in person. This book is also full of games and activities!

Last but not least, I am hidden 9 times on different pages. See how many times you can find me. This page doesn't count!

# Crater Lake Bingo

Let's play bingo! Cross off each box you are able to during your visit to the national park. Try to get a bingo down, across, or diagonally. If you can't visit the park, use the bingo board to plan your perfect trip.

Pick out some activities you would want to do during your visit. What would you do first? How long would you spend there? What animals would you try to see?

| | | | | |
|---|---|---|---|---|
| SPOT A SALAMANDER | SEE SNOW | IDENTIFY A TREE | TAKE A PICTURE AT AN OVERLOOK | WATCH A MOVIE AT THE VISITORS CENTER |
| GO FOR A HIKE | LEARN ABOUT THE INDIGENOUS PEOPLE WHO LIVE IN THIS AREA | WITNESS A SUNRISE OR SUNSET | OBSERVE THE NIGHT SKIES | GO SNOWSHOEING |
| HEAR A BIRD CALL | SPOT A CLEAR BLUE LAKE | FREE SPACE | LEARN HOW CRATER LAKE WAS FORMED | VISIT A RANGER STATION |
| PICK UP TEN PIECES OF TRASH | GO CAMPING | SEE A MULE DEER | VISIT CLEETWOOD COVE | SPOT A BIRD OF PREY |
| LEARN ABOUT THE GEOLOGY OF THE CASCADES | SEE SOMEONE RIDING A HORSE | HAVE A PICNIC | SPOT SOME ANIMAL TRACKS | PARTICIPATE IN A RANGER-LED ACTIVITY |

# The National Park Logo

The National Park System has over 400 units in the US. Just like Crater Lake National Park, each location is unique or special in some way. The areas include other national parks, historic sites, monuments, seashores, and other recreation areas.

Each element of the National Park emblem represents something that the National Park Service protects. Fill in each blank below to show what each symbol represents.

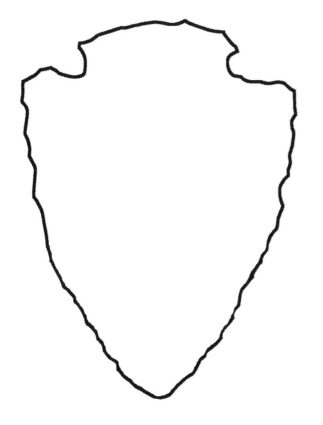

> ### WORD BANK:
> MOUNTAINS, ARROWHEAD, BISON, SEQUOIA TREE, WATER

This represents all plants: _____

This represents all animals: _____

This symbol the landscapes: _____

This represents the waters protected by the park service: _____

This represents the historical and archeological values: _____

Now it's your turn! Pretend you are designing a new national park. Add elements to the design that represent the things your park protects.

What is the name of your park?

Describe why you included the symbols that you chose. What do they mean?

5

# Things To Do Jumble

Unscramble the letters to uncover activities you can do while in Crater Lake National Park. Hint: each one ends in -ing.

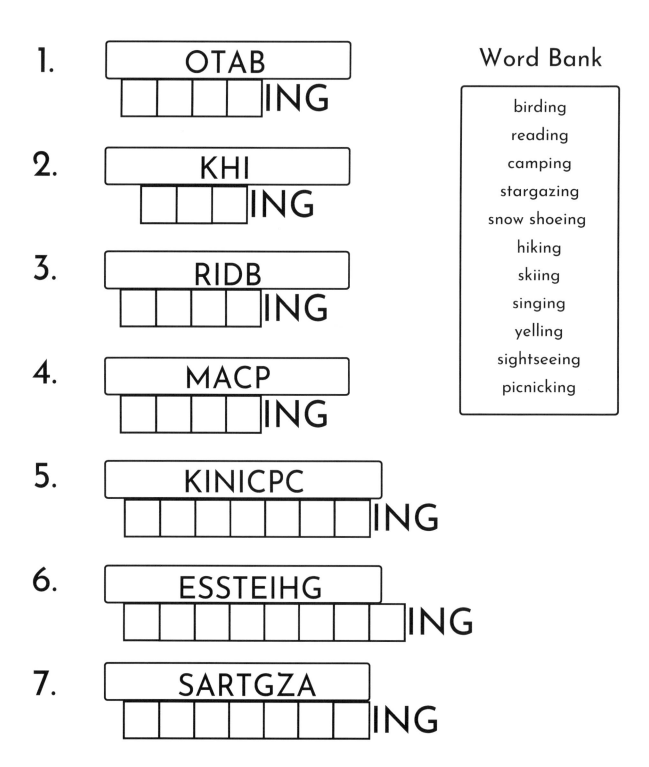

1. OTAB ☐☐☐☐ING

2. KHI ☐☐☐ING

3. RIDB ☐☐☐☐ING

4. MACP ☐☐☐☐ING

5. KINICPC ☐☐☐☐☐☐☐ING

6. ESSTEIHG ☐☐☐☐☐☐☐☐ING

7. SARTGZA ☐☐☐☐☐☐☐ING

## Word Bank

birding
reading
camping
stargazing
snow shoeing
hiking
skiing
singing
yelling
sightseeing
picnicking

# Sound Exploration

Spend a minute or two listening to all of the sounds around you.
Draw your favorite sound.

How did this sound make you feel?

_____

_____

What did you think when you heard this sound?

_____

7

# Go Birdwatching on Rim Drive

start here

**DID YOU KNOW?**

Crater Lake National Park is home to several birds of prey, including eagles, hawks, and owls. Birds of prey are birds that hunt other animals for food.

# Camping Packing List

What should you take with you when you go camping? Pretend you are in charge of your family camping trip. Make a list of what you would need to be safe and comfortable on an overnight excursion. Some considerations are listed on the side.

1.
2.
3.
4.
5.
6.
7.
8.
9.
10.
11.
12.
13.
14.
15.
16.

- What will you eat at every meal?

- What will the weather be like?

- Where will you sleep?

- What will you do during your free time?

- How luxurious do you want camp to be?

- How will you cook?

- How will you see at night?

- How will you dispose of trash?

- What might you need in case of emergencies?

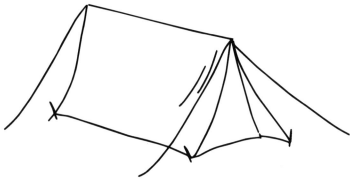

# Crater Lake National Park

Date: _____

Season: _____

Who I went with: _____

Which entrance: _____

How was your experience? Write a few sentences about your trip. Where did you stay? What did you do? What was your favorite activity? If you haven't visited the park yet, write a paragraph pretending that you did.

_____

_____

_____

_____

_____

## STAMPS

Many national parks and monuments have cancellation stamps for visitors to use. These rubber stamps record the date and location that you visited. Many people collect the markings as a free souvenir. Check with a ranger to see where you can find a stamp during your visit. If you aren't able to find one, you can draw your own.

# Where is the Park?

Crater Lake National Park is in the northwest United States. It is located in Oregon.

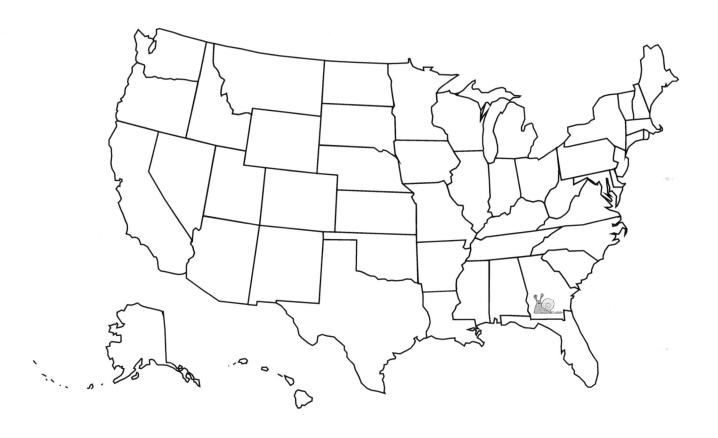

Oregon

Look at the shape of Oregon. Can you find it on the map? If you are from the US, can you find your home state? Color Oregon red. Put a star on the map where you live.

# Connect the Dots #1

Connect the dots to figure out what this tiny critter is. There are five types of these that live in Crater Lake National Park.

Their heart rate can reach as high as 1,260 beats per minute and a breathing rate of 250 breaths per minute. Have you ever measured your breathing rate? Ask a friend or family member to set a timer for 60 seconds. Once they say "go," try to breathe normally. Count each breath until they say "stop." How do your breaths per minute compare to hummingbirds?

_____

_____

Great Egrets are long-legged, long-necked birds adapted for wading in shallow water such as lake edge. They have a wing span of up to 4 1/2 feet.

Bobcats are the most common wildcat in North America. The bobcat is named for its short, bobbed tail.

# Who Lives Here?

Below are 10 plants and animals that live in the park.
Use the word bank to fill in the clues below.

WORD BANK: EGRET, MUSKRAT, BOBCAT, BARRED OWL, OSPREY,
BULL TROUT, ELK, DUCKWEED, VOLE, BITTERCRESS

Muskrats are around the size of a large rat. They are excellent swimmers and can hold their breath underwater for 15-20 minutes.

Bull Trout are members of the char subgroup of the salmon family. They can grow up to 20 lbs in lake environments!

# Common Names
### vs.
# Scientific Names

A common name of an organism is a name that is based on everyday language. You have heard the common names of plants, animals, and other living things on tv, in books, and at school. Common names can also be referred to as "English" names, popular names, or farmer's names. Common names can vary from place to place. The word for a particular tree may be one thing, but that same tree has a different name in another country. Common names can even vary from region to region, even in the same country.

Scientific names, or Latin names, are given to organisms to make it possible to have uniform names for the same species. Scientific names are in Latin. You may have heard plants or animals referred to by their scientific name or parts of their scientific names. Latin names are also called "binomial nomenclature," which refers to a two-part naming system. The first part of the name - the generic name - refers to the genus to which the species belongs. The second part of the name, the specific name, identifies the species. For example, Tyrannosaurus rex is an example of a widely known scientific name.

**American Black Bear**

Ursus americanus

COMMON NAME

**Elk**

Cervus canadensis

# LATIN NAME = GENUS + SPECIES
Elk = Cervus canadensis

Black Bear = Ursus americanus

# Find the Match!
# Common Names and Latin Names

Match the common name to the scientific name for each animal. The first one is done for you. Use clues on the page before and after this one to complete the matches.

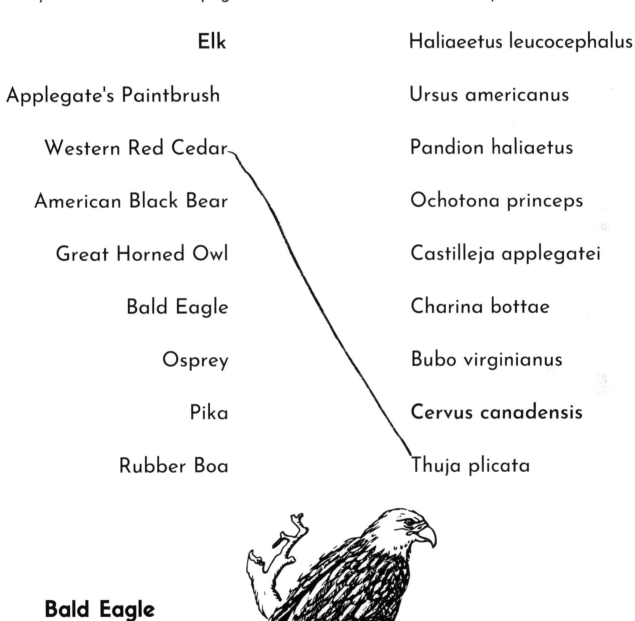

Elk                          Haliaeetus leucocephalus

Applegate's Paintbrush       Ursus americanus

Western Red Cedar            Pandion haliaetus

American Black Bear          Ochotona princeps

Great Horned Owl             Castilleja applegatei

Bald Eagle                   Charina bottae

Osprey                       Bubo virginianus

Pika                         **Cervus canadensis**

Rubber Boa                   Thuja plicata

**Bald Eagle**
Haliaeetus leucocephalus

Osprey
Pandion haliaetus

Bald Eagle
Haliaeetus leucocephalus

Great Horned Owl
Bubo virginianus

**Some plants and animals that live at Crater Lake**

Western Red Cedar
Thuja plicata

Pika
Ochotona princeps

Rubber Boa
Charina bottae

# Weather Watch

Find a place in an open area where you can easily see the sky. Complete the activities below to provide your weather report. If you aren't in the park, you can do this activity from home.

Can you feel any wind?

What does the sky look like?

Is there anything you notice about the weather today?

What is the date?

What is the time?

Where is the sun in the sky? (rising, midpoint, falling)

What direction is the wind blowing?

Are there clouds in the sky? If so, draw them below:

# The Ten Essentials

Careful preparation and knowledge are key to a successful adventure into Crater Lake National Park's backcountry.

The ten essentials are a list of things that are important to have when you go for longer hikes. If you go on a hike in the <u>backcountry</u>, it is especially important that you have everything you need in case of an emergency. If you get lost or something unforeseen happens, it is good to be prepared to survive until help finds you.

The ten essentials list was developed in the 1930s by an outdoors group called the Mountaineers. Over time and technological advancements, this list has evolved. Can you identify all the things on the current list? Circle each of the "essentials" and cross out everything that doesn't make the cut.

| fire: matches, lighter, tinder, and/or stove | a pint of milk | extra money | headlamp, plus extra batteries | extra clothes |
|---|---|---|---|---|
| extra water | a dog | Polaroid camera | bug net | lightweight games, like a deck of cards |
| extra food | a roll of duct tape | shelter | sun protection, such as sunglasses, sun-protective clothes, and sunscreen | knife, plus a gear repair kit |
| a mirror | navigation: map, compass, altimeter, GPS device, or satellite messenger | first aid kit | extra flip-flops | entertainment, such as video games or books |

Backcountry - a remote, undeveloped rural area.

# Rain, Rain, Rain

If it rains while you are visiting Crater Lake National Park, you can do this activity during your trip. If you don't get any rain while you are there, you can follow the same instructions next time it rains where you live.

Go outside into the rain. Use all of your senses as you complete the boxes below. You can use words, drawings, or both.

Sit as still as you can and listen to the rain. How does it make you feel?

Look straight up at the sky and let the raindrops fall on your face. Close your eyes. How does it feel?

Watch where the rain goes. Pay attention to the different surfaces the rain lands on. Which surfaces absorb the rain, and which surfaces cause the rain to run off or pool?

Are there any animals or bugs out enjoying the rain? Do you think the plants are enjoying the rain?

# Connect the Dots #2

This animal lives in almost every state in the US, including the national park. They are nocturnal, more active at night, and sleep during the day. They are omnivorous eaters, meaning they eat both plants and animals.

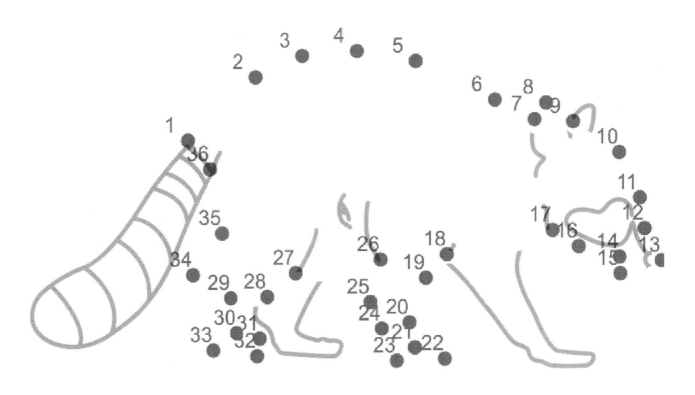

Are you an omnivore like a raccoon? An herbivore only eats plant foods. A carnivore only eats meat. An omnivore eats both. What type of eater are you? Write down some of your favorite foods to back up your answer.

_____

_____

# LISTEN CAREFULLY

Visitors to Crater Lake National Park may hear different noises from those they hear at home. Try this activity to experience this for yourself!

First, find a place outside where it is comfortable to sit or stand for a few minutes. You can do this by yourself or with a friend or family member. Once you have a good spot, close your eyes and listen. Be quiet for one minute and pay attention to what you are hearing. List some of the sounds you have heard in one of the two boxes below:

## NATURAL SOUNDS
MADE BY ANIMALS, TREES OR PLANTS, THE WIND, ETC

## HUMAN-MADE SOUNDS
MADE BY PEOPLE, MACHINES, ETC

## ONCE YOU ARE BACK AT HOME, TRY REPEATING YOUR EXPERIMENT:

### NATURAL SOUNDS
MADE BY ANIMALS, TREES OR PLANTS, THE WIND, ETC

### HUMAN-MADE SOUNDS
MADE BY PEOPLE, MACHINES, ETC

WHERE DID YOU HEAR MORE NATURAL SOUNDS? _____

WHERE DID YOU HEAR MORE HUMAN SOUNDS? _____

# Wildlife Wisdom

The national park is home to many different kinds of animals. Seeing wildlife can be an exciting part of visiting the national park but it is important to remember that these animals are wild. They need plenty of space and a healthy habitat where they can find their own food. Part of this is not allowing animals to eat any human food. This is their home and we are the visitors. We need to be respectful of the wildlife in the park.

Directions: Circle the highlighted words that best complete the following sentences.

If an animal changes its behavior because of your presence, you are:
    A) too close
    B) funny looking
    C) dehydrated and should drink more water

The best thing we can do to help wild animals survive is:
    A) make them pets
    B) protect their habitat
    C) knit them winter sweaters

In a national park, it is okay to share your food with wild animals:
    A) never
    B) always
    C) sometimes

When you're hiking in an area where there are bears, you should warn bears that you are entering their space by:
    A) hiking quietly
    B) making noise
    C) wearing bright colors

At night, park rangers care for the animals by:
    A) putting them back into their cages
    B) tucking them into bed
    C) leaving them alone

If you see an abandoned bird's nest, it is best to:
    A) pet the baby birds
    B) leave it alone
    C) crunch the empty eggshells

Bears look under logs in hopes of finding:
    A) granola bars
    B) insects
    C) peanuts to eat

The place where an animal lives is called its:
    A) condo
    B) habitat
    C) crib

# Crater Lake Word Search

Words may be horizontal, vertical, diagonal,
or they might even be backwards!

1. oregon
2. fog
3. wizard
4. island
5. snow
6. volcano
7. summit
8. godfrey glen
9. marmots
10. the old man
11. cycling
12. phantom ship
13. squirrels
14. aquatic
15. deep
16. blue
17. explorers
18. eagles
19. bobcat
20. mount scott trail

```
C W I L N P N A Q U A T I C K
H I A T M I O E S H E R W R J
T Z P R F O G R C I L P E E D
E A G L E S E U C E S L U M L
C R A I I R R G Q E I L J I L
A D L D Y W O O D B B E A C I
R O A D P R E G A M T R I N N
S Q U I R R E L S W T I K X D
R A H S S U M M I T E D S P E
E L I B O B C A T I N G O T X
C I A H T H E O L D M A N C P
Y C N I K M C I S M O K I R L
C J P I H S M O T N A H P N O
L Y G T T E O N A C L O V E R
I W S N O W A B E S R O H E E
N J U F A R E G L Z E S Q N R
G O D F R E Y G L E N P V E S
M A R M O T S D N Y M A L A S
```

# Find the Match!
## What are Baby Animals Called?

Match the animal to its baby. The first one is done for you.

| | |
|---|---|
| Elk | eaglet |
| Bald Eagle | calf |
| Little Brown Bat | snakelets |
| Striped Skunk | pup |
| Great Horned Owl | owlet |
| Western Toad | kit |
| Mountain Lion | tadpole |
| Garter snake | kitten |

# Design a Badge

Imagine you've been hired to create a badge that will be for sale in the national park gift shop. Your badge will be a souvenir for visitors to remember their trip to the park.

Consider adding a plant or animal that lives here. You could also include a famous place in the park or activity that you can do while visiting.

# The Perfect Picnic Spot

Fill in the blanks on this page without looking at the full story. Once you have each line filled out, use the words you've chosen to complete the story on the next page.

EMOTION _____

FOOD _____

SOMETHING SWEET _____

STORE _____

MODE OF TRANSPORTATION _____

NOUN _____

SOMETHING ALIVE _____

SAUCE _____

PLURAL VEGETABLES _____

ADJECTIVE _____

PLURAL BODY PART _____

ANIMAL _____

PLURAL FRUIT _____

PLACE _____

SOMETHING TALL _____

COLOR _____

ADJECTIVE _____

NOUN _____

A DIFFERENT ANIMAL _____

FAMILY MEMBER #1 _____

FAMILY MEMBER #2 _____

VERB THAT ENDS IN -ING _____

A DIFFERENT FOOD _____

# The Perfect Picnic Spot

Use the words from the previous page to complete a silly story.

When my family suggested having our lunch at the Ponderosa Pine picnic area,

I was _ _ _ _ _ _ _ _. I love eating my _ _ _ _ _ _ outside! I knew we had picked up a
    EMOTION               FOOD

box of _ _ _ _ _ _ from the _ _ _ _ _ _ _ _ for after lunch, my favorite. We drove up
    SOMETHING SWEET       STORE

to the area and I jumped out of the _ _ _ _ _ _ _ _. "I will find the perfect spot for
                    MODE OF TRANSPORTATION

a picnic!" I grabbed a _ _ _ _ _ _ for us to sit on, and I ran off. I passed a picnic
           NOUN

table, but it was covered with _ _ _ _ _ _ _ so we couldn't sit there. The next
               SOMETHING ALIVE

picnic table looked okay, but there were smears of _ _ _ _ _ _ _ and pieces of
                        SAUCE

_ _ _ _ _ _ _ _ everywhere. The people that were there before must have been
PLURAL VEGETABLES

_ _ _ _ _ _! I gritted my _ _ _ _ _ _ _ together and kept walking down the path,
ADJECTIVE       PLURAL BODY PART

determined to find the perfect spot. I wanted a table with a good view of the

trees. Why was this so hard? If we were lucky, I might even get to see _ _ _ _ _ _
                               ANIMAL

eating some _ _ _ _ _ _ on the cliffside. They don't have those in _ _ _ _ _ _ _ where I
     PLURAL FRUIT                      PLACE

am from. I walked down a little hill and there it was, the perfect spot! The trees

towered overhead and looked as tall as _ _ _ _ _ _ _ _. The patch of grass was a
                 SOMETHING TALL

beautiful _ _ _ _ _ _ color. The _ _ _ _ _ _ flowers were growing on
      COLOR         ADJECTIVE

the side of a _ _ _ _ _ _ _. I looked across the lake and even saw a _ _ _ _ _ _ _ _ on
      NOUN                     DIFFERENT ANIMAL

the edge of a rock. I looked back to see my _ _ _ _ _ _ _ _ and _ _ _ _ _ _ _ _
                     FAMILY MEMBER #1    FAMILY MEMBER #2

_ _ _ _ _ _ _ _ a picnic basket. "I hope you brought plenty of _ _ _ _ _ _ _, I'm
VERB THAT ENDS IN ING                     A DIFFERENT FOOD

starving!"

29

# Hike to Cleetwood Cove

start here

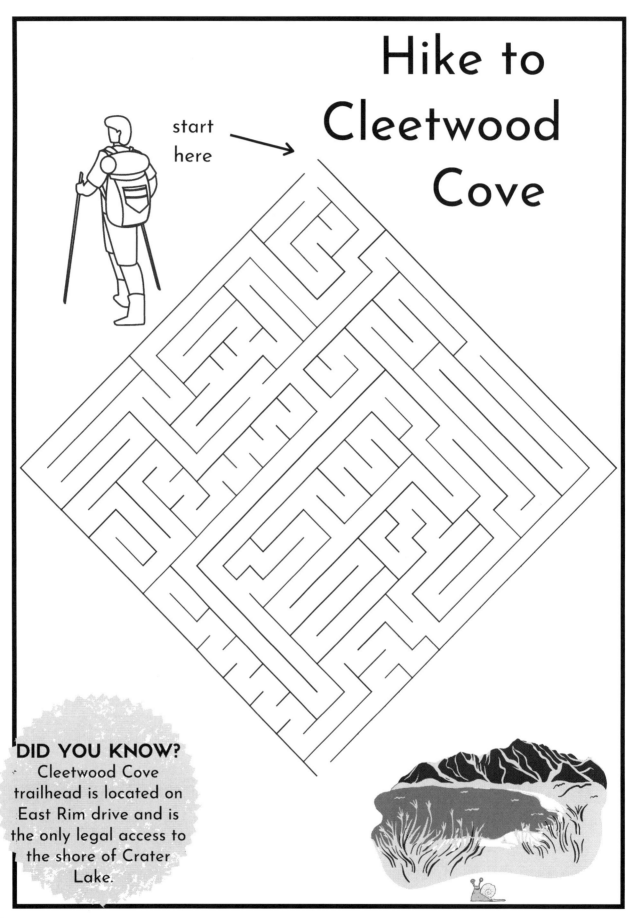

**DID YOU KNOW?**
Cleetwood Cove trailhead is located on East Rim drive and is the only legal access to the shore of Crater Lake.

# Rim Village Historic Distric Word Search

Rim Village is located on the southwestern edge of Crater Lake. It is the main area for tourist services in Crater Lake NP. The landscape is a mixture of designed developed areas and natural areas, including one of the best views of the lake, the Sinnott Memorial Overlook.

1. rim drive
2. rustic
3. mather
4. sinnott
5. thomas vint
6. caldera wall
7. visitors
8. lodge
9. museum
10. promenade
11. kiser studio
12. victor rock
13. stone
14. campground

```
L P R O M E N A D E D E O W C
H A D N U O R G P M A C W R H
T V D N K I T T A W A L M O A
S E U D S C S U C Y U A B M K
C T H O M A S V I N T R S K I
M T D L U L R K C H A E T O S
C O S E S D C E E H L R O A E
A N B E E E I R D I L S N N R
L N H O U R I M D R I V E P S
L I I R M A O Y K U U I R T T
I S A U A W I C N S K S N C U
S H N S K A O I S T S I T R D
T J O S F L I N Z I I T W O I
E Y G E L L V E I C D O V E O
R W E L O O R A D O A R H E M
T T E D G R E E N L A S E N T
U A G E S A E N N O A P V E B
C E V I C T O R R O C K I O N
```

# Leave No Trace Quiz

Leave No Trace is a concept that helps people make decisions during outdoor recreation that protects the environment. There are seven principles that guide us when we spend time outdoors, whether you are in a national park or not. Are you an expert in Leave No Trace? Take this quiz and find out!

1. How can you plan ahead and prepare to ensure you have the best experience you can in the national park?
    a. Make sure you stop by the ranger station for a map and to ask about current conditions.
    b. Just wing it! You will know the best trail when you see it.
    c. Stick to your plan, even if conditions change. You traveled a long way to get here, and you should stick to your plan.
2. What is an example of traveling on a durable surface?
    a. Walking only on the designated path.
    b. Walking on the grass that borders the trail if the trail is very muddy.
    c. Taking a shortcut if you can find one because it means you will be walking less.
3. Why should you dispose of waste properly?
    a. You don't need to. Park rangers love to pick up the trash you leave behind.
    b. You should actually leave your leftovers behind, because animals will eat them. It is important to make sure they aren't hungry.
    c. So that other peoples' experiences of the park are not impacted by you leaving your waste behind.
4. How can you best follow the concept "leave what you find?"
    a. Take only a small rock or leaf to remember your trip.
    b. Take pictures, but leave any physical items where they are.
    c. Leave everything you find, unless it may be rare like an arrowhead, then it is okay to take.
5. What is not a good example of minimizing campfire impacts?
    a. Only having a campfire in a pre-existing campfire ring.
    b. Checking in with current conditions when you consider making a campfire.
    c. Building a new campfire ring in a location that has a better view.
6. What is a poor example of respecting wildlife?
    a. Building squirrel houses out of rocks so the squirrels have a place to live.
    b. Stay far away from wildlife and give them plenty of space.
    c. Reminding your grown-ups not to drive too fast in animal habitats while visiting the park.
7. How can you show consideration of other visitors?
    a. Play music on your speaker so other people at the campground can enjoy it.
    b. Wear headphones on the trail if you choose to listen to music.
    c. Make sure to yell "Hello!" to every animal you see at top volume.

# Park Poetry

America's parks inspire art of all kinds. Painters, sculptors, photographers, writers, and artists of all mediums have taken inspiration from natural beauty. They have turned their inspiration into great works.

Use this space to write your own poem about the park. Think about what you have experienced or seen. Use descriptive language to create an acrostic poem. This type of poem has the first letter of each line spell out another word. Create an acrostic that spells out the word "Lake."

**L** _____

**A** _____

**K** _____

**E** _____

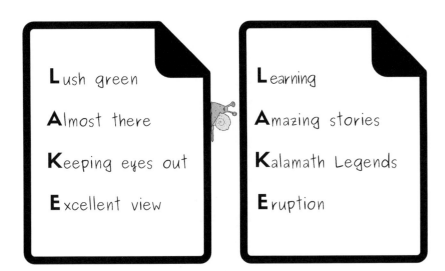

**L**ush green
**A**lmost there
**K**eeping eyes out
**E**xcellent view

**L**earning
**A**mazing stories
**K**alamath Legends
**E**ruption

# Photobook

Draw some pictures of
things you saw in the park.

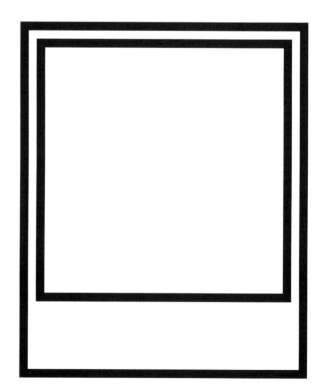

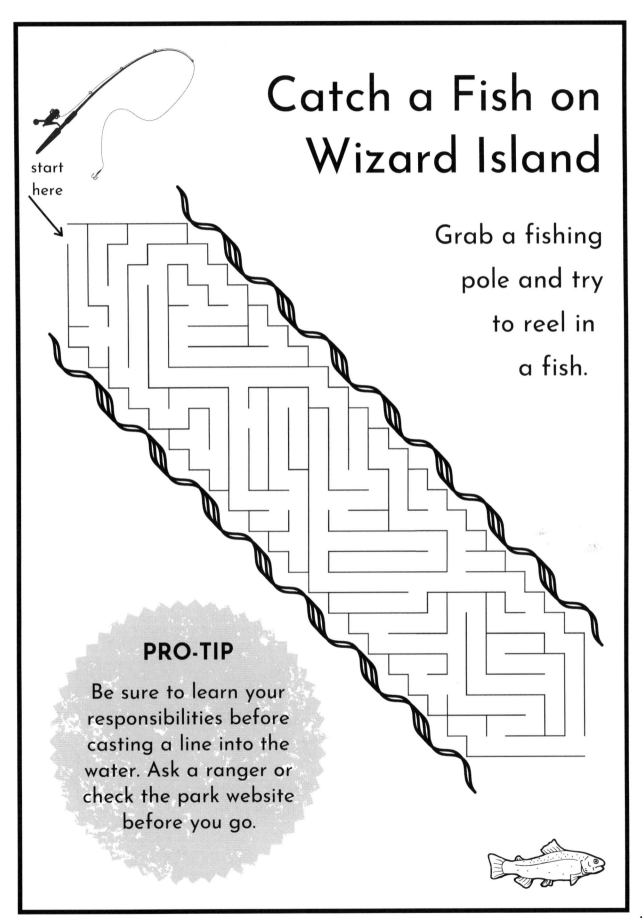

# Catch a Fish on Wizard Island

Grab a fishing pole and try to reel in a fish.

start here

## PRO-TIP

Be sure to learn your responsibilities before casting a line into the water. Ask a ranger or check the park website before you go.

# Stacking Rocks

Have you ever seen stacks of rocks while hiking in national parks? Do you know what they are or what they mean? These rock piles are called cairns and often mark hiking routes in parks. Every park has a different way to maintain trails and cairns. However, they all have the same rule: If you come across a cairn, do not disturb it!

Color the cairn and the rules to remember.

## 1. Do not tamper with cairns.

If a cairn is tampered with or an unauthorized one is built, then future visitors may become disoriented or even lost.

## 2. Do not build unauthorized cairns.

Moving rocks disturbs the soil and makes the area more prone to erosion. Disturbing rocks can disturb fragile plants.

## 3. Do not add to existing cairns.

Authorized cairns are carefully designed. Adding to them can actually cause them to collapse.

# Decoding Using American Sign Language

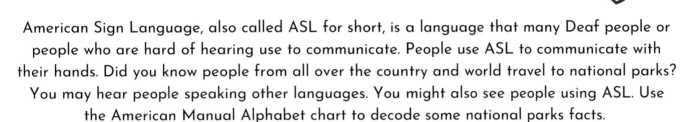

American Sign Language, also called ASL for short, is a language that many Deaf people or people who are hard of hearing use to communicate. People use ASL to communicate with their hands. Did you know people from all over the country and world travel to national parks? You may hear people speaking other languages. You might also see people using ASL. Use the American Manual Alphabet chart to decode some national parks facts.

**This was the first national park to be established:**

**This is the biggest national park in the US:**

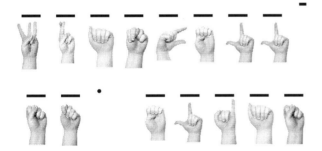

**This is the most visited national park:**

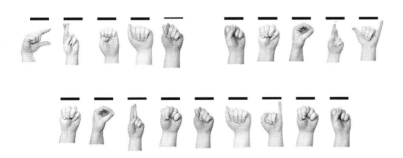

Hint: Pay close attention to the position of the thumb!

Try it! Using the chart, try to make the letters of the alphabet with your hand. What is the hardest letter to make? Can you spell out your name? Show a friend or family member and have them watch you spell out the name of the national park you are in.

# Go Horseback Riding on the Pacific Crest Trail

Help find the horse's lost shoe!

**DID YOU KNOW?**

Horseback riding is a popular activity in Crater Lake National Park. There are many trails that you can take horses for day or overnight trips.

start here

# Butterflies of the Cascades

Dozens of species of butterflies and moths live in Crater Lake National Park. Their wingspan size varies, as do the patterns on their wings. Design your own butterfly below. Make sure the wings are symmetrical, which means both sides match.

# A Hike to Cleetwood Cove

Fill in the blanks on this page without looking at the full story. Once you have each line filled out, use the words you've chosen to complete the story on the next page.

ADJECTIVE _____

SOMETHING TO EAT _____

SOMETHING TO DRINK _____

NOUN _____

ARTICLE OF CLOTHING _____

BODY PART _____

VERB _____

ANIMAL _____

SAME TYPE OF FOOD _____

ADJECTIVE _____

SAME ANIMAL _____

VERB THAT ENDS IN "ED" _____

NUMBER _____

A DIFFERENT NUMBER _____

SOMETHING THAT FLIES _____

LIGHT SOURCE _____

PLURAL NOUN _____

FAMILY MEMBER _____

YOUR NICKNAME _____

# A Hike at Cleetwood Cove

Use the words from the previous page to complete a silly story.

I went for a hike at Cleetwood Cove today. In my favorite _____
                                                          ADJECTIVE

backpack, I made sure to pack a map so I wouldn't get lost. I also threw in an

extra _____ just in case I got hungry and a bottle of _____.
      SOMETHING TO EAT                                       SOMETHING TO DRINK

I put on my _____ spray, and I tied a _____ around my
            NOUN                           ARTICLE OF CLOTHING

_____, in case it gets chilly. I started to _____ down the path. As
BODY PART                                         VERB

soon as I turned the corner, I came face to face with a(n) _____. I think
                                                          ANIMAL

it was as startled as I was! What should I do? I had to think fast! Should I

give it some of my _____? No. I had to remember what the
                   SAME TYPE OF FOOD

_____ ranger told me: "If you see one, back away slowly and try not to
ADJECTIVE

scare it." Soon enough, the _____ _____ away. The coast
                            SAME ANIMAL   VERB THAT ENDS IN ED

was clear. _____ hours later, I finally got to the lookout. I felt like I could
          NUMBER

see for a _____ miles. I took a picture of a _____ so I could always
         A DIFFERENT NUMBER                    NOUN

remember this moment. As I was putting my camera away, a _____
                                                         SOMETHING THAT FLIES

flew by, reminding me that it was almost nighttime. I turned on my

_____ and headed back. I could hear the _____ singing their
LIGHT SOURCE                                  PLURAL INSECT

evening song. Just as I was getting tired, I saw my _____ and our tent.
                                                   FAMILY MEMBER

"Welcome back _____! How was your hike?"
              NICKNAME

# Bird Scavenger Hunt

Crater Lake National Park is a great place to go birdwatching. You don't have to be able to identify different species of birds in order to have fun. Open your eyes and tune in your ears. Check off as many birds on this list as you can.

☐ A colorful bird      ☐ A big bird

☐ A brown bird      ☐ A small bird

☐ A bird in a tree      ☐ A hopping bird

☐ A bird with long tail feathers      ☐ A flying bird

☐ A bird making noise      ☐ A bird's nest

☐ A bird eating or hunting      ☐ A bird's footprint on the ground

☐ A bird with spots      ☐ A bird with stripes somewhere on it

What was the easiest bird on the list to find? What was the hardest? Why do you think that was?

_____

_____

_____

# Let's Go Camping
# Word Search

Words may be horizontal, vertical, diagonal, or they might even be backwards!

1. tent
2. camp stove
3. sleeping bag
4. bug spray
5. sunscreen
6. map
7. flashlight
8. pillow
9. lantern
10. ice
11. snacks
12. smores
13. water
14. first aid kit
15. chair
16. cards
17. books
18. games
19. trail
20. hat

```
D P P I L L O W D B T E A C I
E O A D P R E A A M B R C A N
P W C A M P S T O V E I H X G
R A H S G E L E B E E D A P S
E L B U G S P R A Y N G I E A
S I A H G C I C N N M E R C N
C W N L A F I R S K O O B F K
M T A E M I L E L H M R W L J
T A P R E A O R E S L B A A B
S M P A S R R T E N T L U S C
C E A I I R C G P E I U J H A
S S N A C K S S I M O K I L R
I J R S F O I S N J R A Q I D
C Y E T L E V E G U O R V G S
E W T A K C A B B S S O H H M
X J N F I R S T A I D K I T T
U A A E S S E N G E T P V A B
C J L I A R T D N A M A H A S
```

# All in the Day of a Park Ranger

Park Rangers are hardworking individuals dedicated to protecting our parks, monuments, museums, and more. They take care of the natural and cultural resources for future generations. Rangers also help protect the visitors of the park. Their responsibilities are broad and they work both with the public and behind the scenes.

What have you seen park rangers do? Use your knowledge of the duties of park rangers to fill out a typical daily schedule, listing one activity for each hour. Feel free to make up your own, but some examples of activities are provided on the right. Read carefully! Not all the example activities are befitting a ranger.

|  |  |
|------|----------|
| 6 am | Lead a sunrise hike |
| 7 am | |
| 8 am | |
| 9 am | |
| 10 am | |
| 11 am | |
| 12 pm | Enjoy a lunch break outside |
| 1 pm | |
| 2 pm | |
| 3 pm | |
| 4 pm | Teach visitors about the geology of the mountain |
| 5 pm | |
| 6 pm | |
| 7 pm | |
| 8 pm | |
| 9 pm | |

- feed the bald eagles
- build trails for visitors to enjoy
- throw rocks off the side of the mountain
- rescue lost hikers
- study animal behavior
- record air quality data
- answer questions at the visitor center
- pick wildflowers
- pick up litter
- share marshmallows with squirrels
- repair handrails
- lead a class on a field trip
- catch frogs and make them race
- lead people on educational hikes
- write articles for the park website
- protect the river from pollution
- remove non-native plants from the park
- study how climate change is affecting the park
- give a talk about mountain lions
- lead a program for campers on salmon

If you were a park ranger, which of the above tasks would you enjoy most?

_____

_____

# Draw Yourself as a Park Ranger

# The Animals of Crater Lake

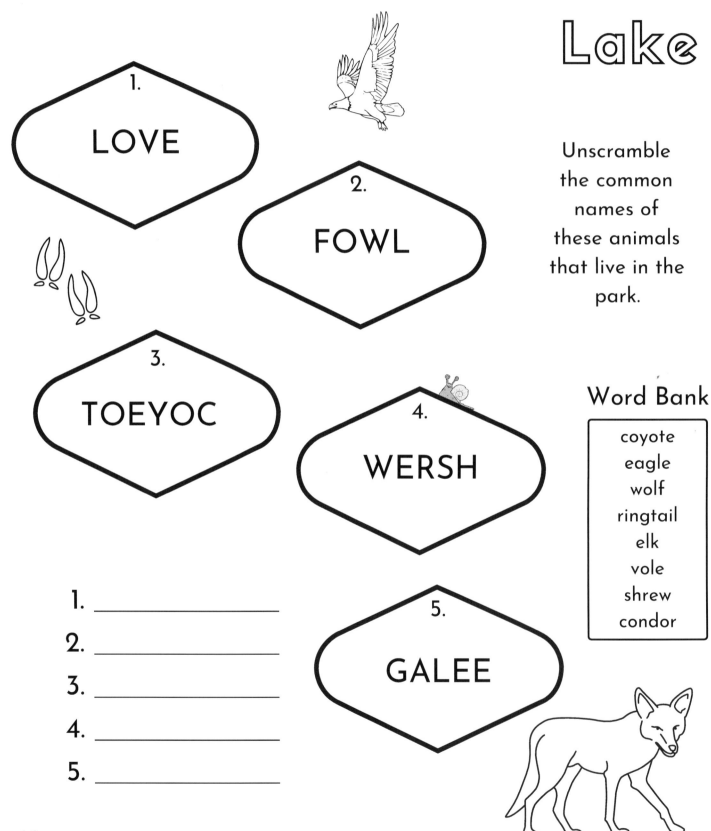

**1.** LOVE

**2.** FOWL

Unscramble the common names of these animals that live in the park.

**3.** TOEYOC

**4.** WERSH

**5.** GALEE

### Word Bank

coyote
eagle
wolf
ringtail
elk
vole
shrew
condor

1. _____
2. _____
3. _____
4. _____
5. _____

# Amphibians

One species of toad and three species of frogs live in Crater Lake Park. Crater Lake is the only place in the world that you will find the Crater Lake newt! Frogs and toads both spend the beginning of their lives the same way - as tadpoles. Tadpoles hatch from eggs, usually in springs or pools of water.

Both frogs and toads are amphibians. Color the amphibians below.

# Making a Difference

It is important to protect the valuable resources of the world, not just beautiful places like national parks.

How many of these things do you do at home? If you answered "no" to more than 10 items, talk to the grownups in your life to see if there are any household habits you might be able to change. Conserving our collective resources helps us all.

| Yes | No | Do you… |
|-----|-----|---------|
| ☐ | ☐ | turn off the water when brushing your teeth? |
| ☐ | ☐ | use LED light bulbs when possible? |
| ☐ | ☐ | use a reusable water bottle instead of disposable ones? |
| ☐ | ☐ | ride your bike or take the bus instead of riding in the car? |
| ☐ | ☐ | have a rain barrel under your roof gutters to collect rain water? |
| ☐ | ☐ | take quick showers? |
| ☐ | ☐ | avoid putting more food on your plate than you will eat? |
| ☐ | ☐ | take reusable lunch containers? |
| ☐ | ☐ | grow a garden? |
| ☐ | ☐ | buy items with less packaging? |
| ☐ | ☐ | recycle paper? |
| ☐ | ☐ | recycle plastic? |
| ☐ | ☐ | have a compost pile at home so you can make your own soil? |
| ☐ | ☐ | pick up trash when you see it on the trail? |
| ☐ | ☐ | plan a "staycation" and fly only when you have to? |

| # of Yes | # of No |
|----------|---------|

Add up your score! Are there any "no"s that you want to turn into a yes?

**Can you think of any other ways to protect our natural resources?**

# Bear Aware

Bears in the wild have plenty of things to eat! When you are in bear country, it is especially important to keep bears safe by making sure they can't eat any human food. When you are camping, you should store your food in special bear boxes. These metal storage boxes are animal-proof and will prevent wildlife from getting to your food.

Draw a line from each item to either the bear (if it is safe for bears to eat it) or to the bear box (if it needs to be stored.)

49

# 63 National Parks

How many other national parks have you been to? Which one do you want to visit next? Note that if some of these parks fall on the border of more than one state, you may check it off more than once!

### Alaska
- [ ] Denali National Park
- [ ] Gates of the Arctic National Park
- [ ] Glacier Bay National Park
- [ ] Katmai National Park
- [ ] Kenai Fjords National Park
- [ ] Kobuk Valley National Park
- [ ] Lake Clark National Park
- [ ] Wrangell-St. Elias National Park

### American Samoa
- [ ] National Park of American Samoa

### Arizona
- [ ] Grand Canyon National Park
- [ ] Petrified Forest National Park
- [ ] Saguaro National Park

### Arkansas
- [ ] Hot Springs National Park

### California
- [ ] Channel Islands National Park
- [ ] Death Valley National Park
- [ ] Joshua Tree National Park
- [ ] Kings Canyon National Park
- [ ] Lassen Volcanic National Park
- [ ] Pinnacles National Park
- [ ] Redwood National Park
- [ ] Sequoia National Park
- [ ] Yosemite National Park

### Colorado
- [ ] Black Canyon of the Gunnison National Park
- [ ] Great Sand Dunes National Park
- [ ] Mesa Verde National Park
- [ ] Rocky Mountain National Park

### Florida
- [ ] Biscayne National Park
- [ ] Dry Tortugas National Park
- [ ] Everglades National Park

### Hawaii
- [ ] Haleakala National Park
- [ ] Hawai'i Volcanoes National Park

### Idaho
- [ ] Yellowstone National Park

### Kentucky
- [ ] Mammoth Cave National Park

### Indiana
- [ ] Indiana Dunes National Park

### Maine
- [ ] Acadia National Park

### Michigan
- [ ] Isle Royale National Park

### Minnesota
- [ ] Voyageurs National Park

### Missouri
- [ ] Gateway Arch National Park

### Montana
- [ ] Glacier National Park
- [ ] Yellowstone National Park

### Nevada
- [ ] Death Valley National Park
- [ ] Great Basin National Park

### New Mexico
- [ ] Carlsbad Caverns National Park
- [ ] White Sands National Park

### North Dakota
- [ ] Theodore Roosevelt National Park

### North Carolina
- [ ] Great Smoky Mountains National Park

### Ohio
- [ ] Cuyahoga Valley National Park

### Oregon
- [ ] Crater Lake National Park

### South Carolina
- [ ] Congaree National Park

### South Dakota
- [ ] Badlands National Park
- [ ] Wind Cave National Park

### Tennessee
- [ ] Great Smoky Mountains National Park

### Texas
- [ ] Big Bend National Park
- [ ] Guadalupe Mountains National Park

### Utah
- [ ] Arches National Park
- [ ] Bryce Canyon National Park
- [ ] Canyonlands National Park
- [ ] Capitol Reef National Park
- [ ] Zion National Park

### Virgin Islands
- [ ] Virgin Islands National Park

### Virginia
- [ ] Shenandoah National Park

### Washington
- [ ] Mount Rainier National Park
- [ ] North Cascades National Park
- [ ] Olympic National Park

### West Virginia
- [ ] New River Gorge National Park

### Wyoming
- [ ] Grand Teton National Park
- [ ] Yellowstone National Park

# Other National Parks Crossword

Besides Crater Lake National Park, there are 62 other diverse and beautiful national parks across the United States. Try your hand at this crossword. If you need help, look at the previous page for some hints.

## Down

1. State where Acadia National Park is located
2. This national park has the Spanish word for turtle in it
3. Number of national parks in Alaska
5. This national park has some of the hottest temperatures in the world
6. This national park is the only one in Idaho
7. This toothsome creature can famously be found in Everglades National Park
8. Only president with a national park named for them

## Across

4. This state has the most national parks.
9. This park has some of the newest land in the US, caused by volcanic eruptions.
10. This park has the deepest lake in the United States.
11. This color shows up in the name of a national park in California.
12. This national park deserves a gold medal.

# Which National Park Will You Go To Next?
## Word Search

1. Zion
2. Big Bend
3. Glacier
4. Olympic
5. Sequoia
6. Bryce
7. Mesa Verde
8. Biscayne
9. Wind Cave
10. Great Basin
11. Katmai
12. Yellowstone
13. Voyageurs
14. Arches
15. Badlands
16. Denali
17. Glacier Bay
18. Hot Springs

```
F M M E S A V E R D E B N E Y
E A B I G B E N D E S A S E M
Y L I C A L O Y N E E D L T G
D M G A S S A U C N R L U E R
C E L I I T S C R E O A A K E
S N A W Y E E O I W T N A C A
G I C H A A Q C S E M D N S T
N O I Z P R U T I M R S N E B
I W E L M P O N B W E B K H A
R J R F D N I F L I H B U C S
P A B E E S A N E S O P W R I
S J A E N Y A C S I B A U A N
T C Y I A D O H H Y M E A L R
O T A T L M L E S E G R W R J
H S T O I K A T M A I R O P B
I C H U R C O L Y M P I C O U
O Y G T S D E O S B R Y C E T
W I N D C A V E I N R O H E M
```

52

# Field Notes

Spend some time reflecting on your trip to Crater Lake National Park. Your field notes will help you remember the things you experienced. Use the space below to write about your day.

While I was at Crater Lake National Park...

I saw:

_____

_____

_____

_____

I heard:

_____

_____

_____

I felt:

_____

Draw a picture of your favorite thing in the park.

_____

_____

I wondered:

_____

_____

_____

_____

# ANSWER KEY

# National Park Emblem Answers

1. This represents all plants: **Sequoia Tree**

2. This represents all animals: **Bison**

3. This symbol represents the landscapes: **Mountains**

4. This represents the waters protected by the park service: **Water**

5. This represents the historical and archeological values: **Arrowhead**

# Jumbles Answers

1. BOATING

2. HIKING

3. BIRDING

4. CAMPING

5. PICNICKING

6. SIGHTSEEING

7. STAR GAZING

# Go Birdwatching on Rim Drive

start here

**DID YOU KNOW?**
Crater Lake NP is home to several birds of prey, including eagles, hawks, and owls. Birds of prey are birds that hunt other animals for food.

# Answers: Who Lives Here?

Below are 10 plants and animals that live in the park.
Use the word bank to fill in the clues below.

WORD BANK: EGRET, MUSKRAT, BOBCAT, BARRED OWL, OSPREY,
BULL TROUT, ELK, DUCKWEED, VOLE, BITTERCRESS

BITTER **C** RESS

EG **R** ET

BOBC **A** T

BULL█ **T** ROUT

BARR **E** D█OWL

OSP **R** EY

E **L** K

MUSKR **A** T

DUC **K** WEED

VOL **E**

# Find the Match!
# Common Names and Latin Names

Match the common name to the scientific name for each animal. The first one is done for you. Use clues on the page before and after this one to complete the matches.

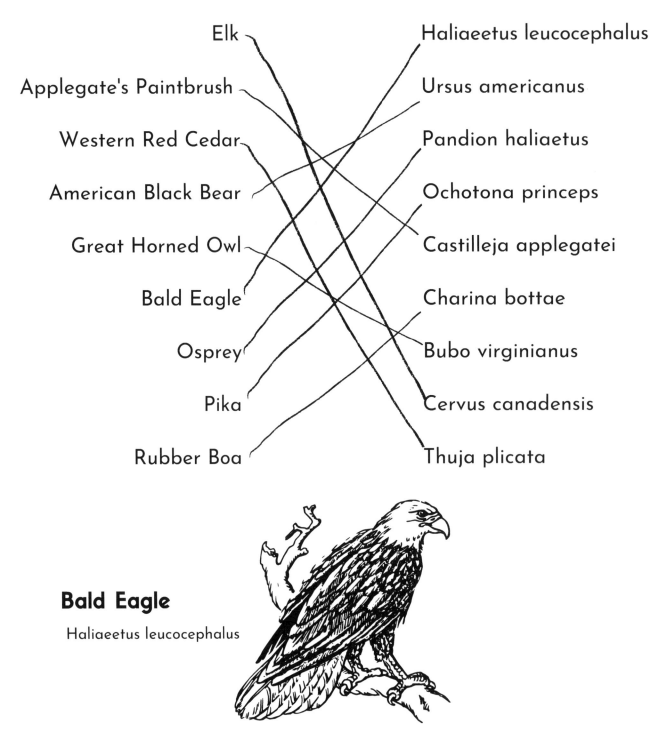

Elk     Haliaeetus leucocephalus

Applegate's Paintbrush     Ursus americanus

Western Red Cedar     Pandion haliaetus

American Black Bear     Ochotona princeps

Great Horned Owl     Castilleja applegatei

Bald Eagle     Charina bottae

Osprey     Bubo virginianus

Pika     Cervus canadensis

Rubber Boa     Thuja plicata

**Bald Eagle**

Haliaeetus leucocephalus

# Answers: The Ten Essentials

Careful preparation and knowledge are key to a successful adventure into Crater Lake National Park's backcountry.

The ten essentials are a list of things that are important to have when you go for longer hikes. If you go on a hike to the <u>backcountry</u>, it is especially important that you have everything you need in case of an emergency. If you get lost or something unforeseen happens, it is good to be prepared to survive until help finds you.

The ten essentials list was developed in the 1930s by an outdoors group called the Mountaineers. Over time and technological advancements, this list has evolved. Can you identify all the things on the current list? Circle each of the "essentials" and cross out everything that doesn't make the cut.

**Backcountry - a remote undeveloped rural area.**

# Crater Lake Word Search

Words may be horizontal, vertical, diagonal,
or they might be backwards!

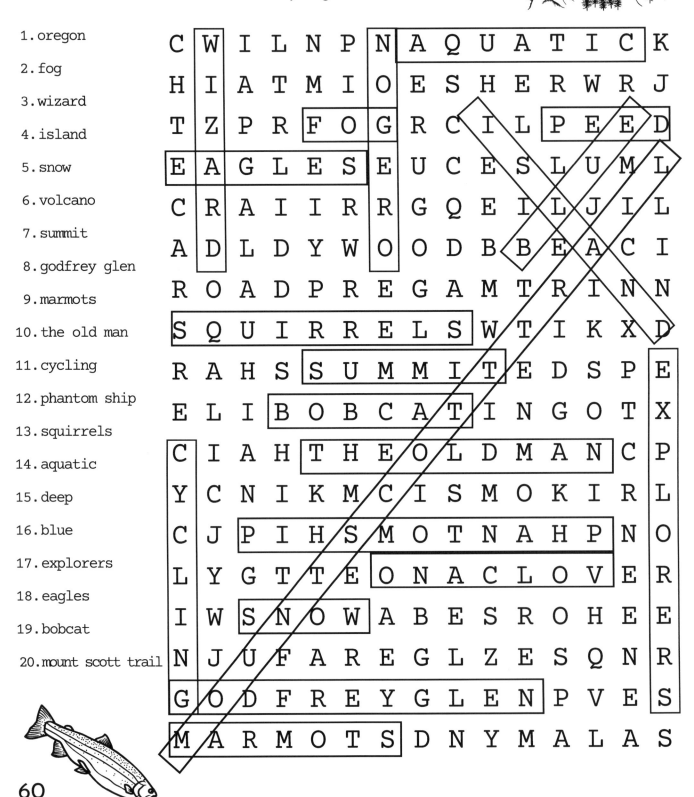

1. oregon
2. fog
3. wizard
4. island
5. snow
6. volcano
7. summit
8. godfrey glen
9. marmots
10. the old man
11. cycling
12. phantom ship
13. squirrels
14. aquatic
15. deep
16. blue
17. explorers
18. eagles
19. bobcat
20. mount scott trail

# Answers: Find the Match!
# What are Baby Animals Called?

Match the animal to its baby. The first one is done for you.

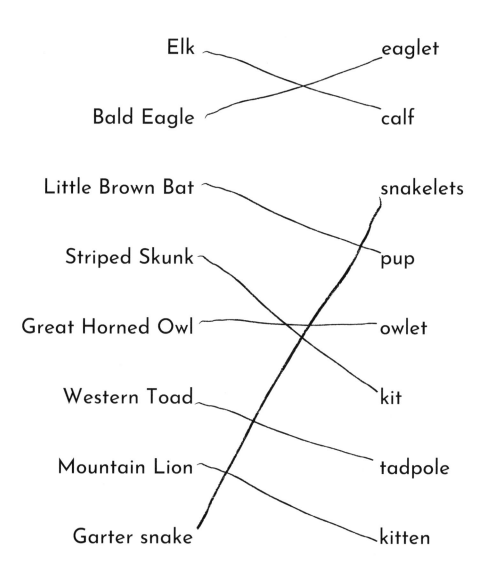

Elk            eaglet

Bald Eagle           calf

Little Brown Bat        snakelets

Striped Skunk         pup

Great Horned Owl     owlet

Western Toad          kit

Mountain Lion        tadpole

Garter snake         kitten

# Solution: Hike to Cleetwood Cove

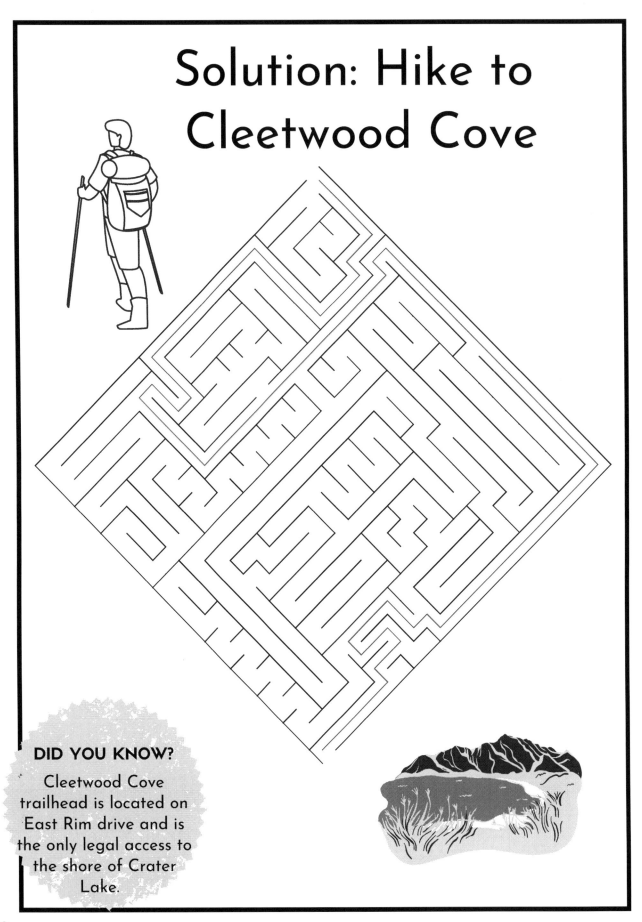

**DID YOU KNOW?**

Cleetwood Cove trailhead is located on East Rim drive and is the only legal access to the shore of Crater Lake.

# Rim Village Historic Distric Word Search

Rim Village is located on the southwestern edge of Crater Lake. It is the main area for tourist services in Crater Lake NP. The landscape is a mixture of designed developed areas and natural areas, including one of the best views of the lake, the Sinnott Memorial Overlook.

1. rim drive
2. rustic
3. mather
4. sinnott
5. thomas vint
6. caldera wall
7. visitors
8. lodge
9. museum
10. promenade
11. kiser studio
12. victor rock
13. stone
14. campground

```
L P R O M E N A D E D E O W C
H A D N U O R G P M A C W R H
T V D N K I T T A W A L M O A
S E U D S C S U C Y U A B M K
C T H O M A S V I N T R S K I
M T D L U L R K C H A E T O S
C O S E S D C E E H L R O A E
A N B E E E I R D I L S N N R
L N H O U R I M D R I V E P S
L I I R M A O Y K U U I R T T
I S A U A W I C N S K S N C U
S H N S K A O I S T S I T R D
T J O S F L I N Z I I T W O I
E Y G E L L V E I C D O V E O
R W E L O O R A D O A R H E M
T T E D G R E E N L A S E N T
U A G E S A E N N O A P V E B
C E V I C T O R R O C K I O N
```

63

# Answers: Leave No Trace Quiz

Leave No Trace is a concept that helps people make decisions during outdoor recreation that protects the environment. There are seven principles that guide us when we spend time outdoors, whether you are in a national park or not. Are you an expert in Leave No Trace? Take this quiz and find out!

1. How can you plan ahead and prepare to ensure you have the best experience you can in the National Park?

    A. Make sure you stop by the ranger station for a map and to ask about current conditions.

2. What is an example of traveling on a durable surface?

    A. Walking only on the designated path.

3. Why should you dispose of waste properly?

    C. So that other peoples' experiences of the park are not impacted by you leaving your waste behind.

4. How can you best follow the concept "leave what you find?"

    B. Take pictures but leave any physical items where they are.

5. What is not a good example of minimizing campfire impacts?

    C. Building a new campfire ring in a location that has a better view.

6. What is a poor example of respecting wildlife?

    A. Building squirrel houses out of rocks from the river so the squirrels have a place to live.

7. How can you show consideration of other visitors?

    B. Wear headphones on the trail if you choose to listen to music.

# Solution: Catch a Fish on Wizard Island

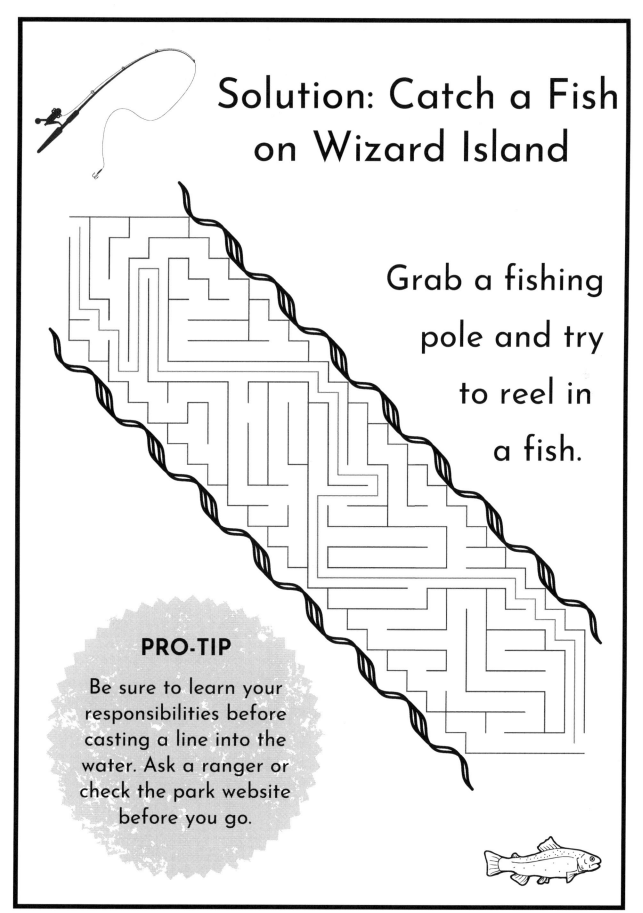

Grab a fishing pole and try to reel in a fish.

**PRO-TIP**

Be sure to learn your responsibilities before casting a line into the water. Ask a ranger or check the park website before you go.

# Decoding Using American Sign Language

American Sign Language, also called ASL for short, is a language that many Deaf people or people who are hard of hearing use to communicate. People use ASL to communicate with their hands. Did you know people from all over the country and world travel to national parks? You may hear people speaking other languages. You might also see people using ASL. Use the American Manual Alphabet chart to decode some national parks facts.

This was the first national park to be established:

## Y E L L O W S T O N E

This is the biggest national park in the US:

## W R A N G E L L -

## S T . E L I A S

This is the most visited national park:

## G R E A T S M O K Y

## M O U N T A I N S

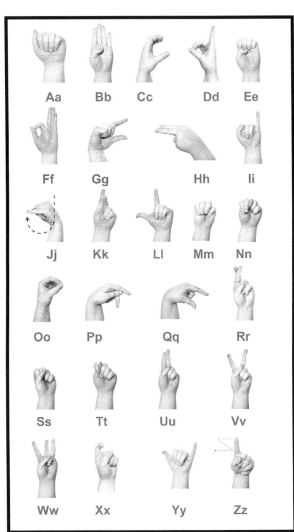

Hint: Pay close attention to the position of the thumb!

Try it! Using the chart, try to make the letters of the alphabet with your hand. What is the hardest letter to make? Can you spell out your name? Show a friend or family member and have them watch you spell out the name of the national park you are in.

# Go Horseback Riding on the Pacific Crest Trail

Help find the horse's lost shoe!

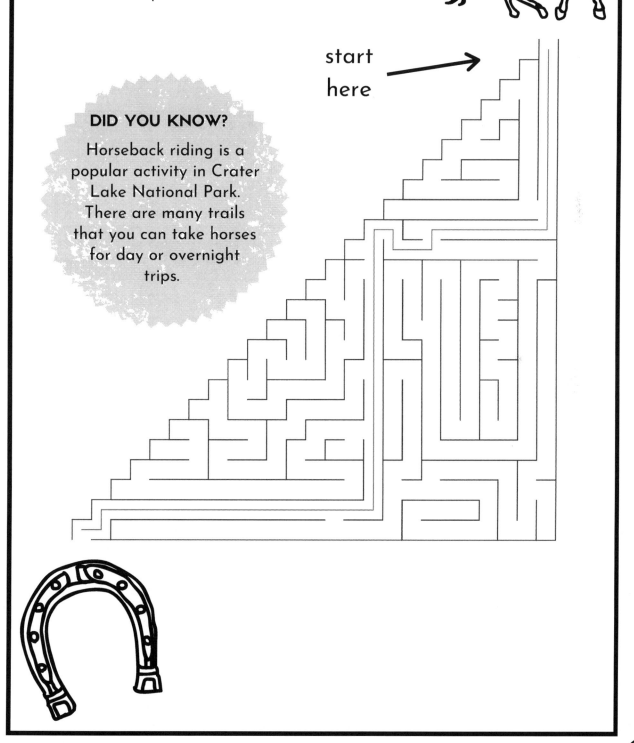

**DID YOU KNOW?**

Horseback riding is a popular activity in Crater Lake National Park. There are many trails that you can take horses for day or overnight trips.

start here

# Let's Go Camping Word Search

1. tent
2. camp stove
3. sleeping bag
4. bug spray
5. sunscreen
6. map
7. flashlight
8. pillow
9. lantern
10. ice
11. snacks
12. smores
13. water
14. first aid kit
15. chair
16. cards
17. books
18. games
19. trail
20. hat

```
D P P I L L O W D B T E A C I
E O A D P R E A A M B R C A N
P W C A M P S T O V E I H X G
R A H S G E L E B E E D A P S
E L B U G S P R A Y N G I E A
S I A H G C I C N N M E R C N
C W N L A F I R S K O O B F K
M T A E M I L E L H M R W L J
T A P R E A O R E S L B A A B
S M P A S R R T E N T L U S C
C E A I I R C G P E I U J H A
S S N A C K S S I M O K I L R
I J R S F O I S N J R A Q I D
C Y E T L E V E G U O R V G S
E W T A K C A B B S S O H H M
X J N F I R S T A I D K I T T
U A A E S S E N G E T P V A B
C J L I A R T D N A M A H A S
```

68

# All in the Day of a Park Ranger

There are many right answers for this activity, but not all of the provided examples are good activities for a park ranger. In fact, a park ranger's job may include stopping visitors from doing some of these things.

**The list below has activities that rangers do not do:**

feed the migratory birds

throw rocks off the side of the mountain

pick wildflowers

share marshmallows with squirrels

catch frogs or toads and make them race

# Animals of Crater Lake

1. __VOLE__
2. __WOLF__
3. __COYOTE__
4. __SHREW__
5. __EAGLE__

# Answers: Other National Parks Crossword

## Down

1. State where Acadia National Park is located
2. This National Park has the Spanish word for turtle in it
3. Number of National Parks in Alaska
5. This National Park has some of the hottest temperatures in the world
6. This National Park is the only one in Idaho
7. This toothsome creature can be famously found in Everglades National Park
8. Only president with a national park named for them

## Across

4. This state has the most National Parks
9. This park has some of the newest land in the US, caused by a volcanic eruption
10. This park has the deepest lake in the United States
11. This color shows up in the name of a National Park in California
12. This National Park deserves a gold medal

# Answers: Which National Park Will You Go To Next?

1. Zion
2. Big Bend
3. Glacier
4. Olympic
5. Sequoia
6. Bryce
7. Mesa Verde
8. Biscayne
9. Wind Cave
10. Great Basin
11. Katmai
12. Yellowstone
13. Voyageurs
14. Arches
15. Badlands
16. Denali
17. Glacier Bay
18. Hot Springs

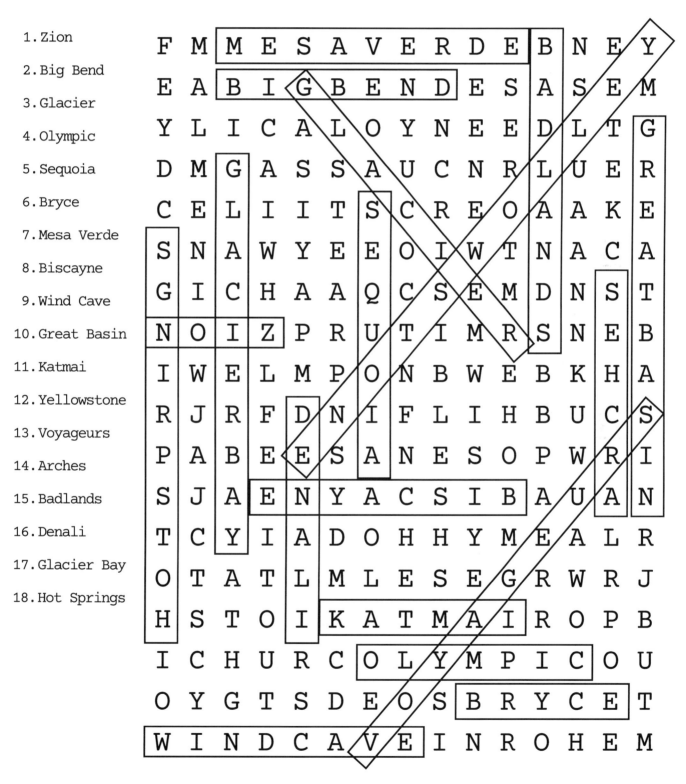

Little Bison Press is an independent children's book publisher based in the Pacific Northwest. We promote exploration, conservation, and adventure through our books. Established in 2021, our passion for outside spaces and travel inspired the creation of Little Bison Press.

We seek to publish books that support children in learning about and caring for the natural places in our world.

To learn more, visit:
## www.littlebisonpress.com

Want more free games and activities? Visit our website!

Made in United States
Troutdale, OR
08/22/2023

12288417R00042